TWO TERMITES ON NOAH'S ARK

a tale for navigating difficult times

Keep gnawing.
Bonsai Cox

story by

BONSAI COX

illustrations by

ALAN WERNER

Book design by Meradith Kill | The Troy Book Makers
Illustrations by Alan Werner

Printed in the United States of America

The Troy Book Makers • Troy, New York • thetroybookmakers.com

To order additional copies of this title, contact your favorite local bookstore
or visit www.shoptbmbooks.com

ISBN: 978-1-61468-497-8

DEDICATED TO

WOODY AND DUSTIE

"We can do this! We're almost there," Dustie said. She and Woody were a mile away from the termite colony that had always been their home.

"I hope we're not too late," Woody said.

Dustie glanced up at the clear blue sky.

"Not a rain cloud in sight," she said. "We'll make it in time."

"Before the rain, yes. But what if Noah has already chosen two other termites?"

"I don't think so. No other colony is as close to the boat as ours."

They kept walking until the temperature dropped so suddenly they both stopped and looked around.

"That boat casts a mighty big shadow," Dustie said.

"It's even bigger than I imagined," Woody said. "Hey! What's that noise?"

He turned toward the sound and saw two elephants going up a sturdy, wide ramp. It creaked under their weight. A few people and a huge number of animals gathered near the foot of the ramp.

"That must be where everybody gets on board," Woody added. "Let's go!"

Soon they stood at the edge of the crowd of animals.

"What's up?" Dustie asked a porcupine who was standing at the foot of the ramp. The porcupine looked around.

"Oh, you guys are small! I didn't see you at first," the porcupine said. "That's Noah up there, the human at the center of the activity. He's the one taking care of everything for all of us."

"So that's Noah!" Woody said. "We heard about a week ago that he expects torrential rains, high winds, and a huge flood to hit the area soon."

"He built this boat because he believes the water will rise and cover all the land," Dustie said.

"He and his family worked on it for over a year. He calls it the ark," said the second porcupine.

"We heard that its purpose is to save all the creatures: large and small, feathery, leathery, scaly, furry, boneless, and hard shelled," Dustie said. "All kinds are welcome, but there's only room for two of every species. So we talked with our family and friends, said our goodbyes, and started on our journey."

"When I first heard about it," Woody added, "I wondered how he would select just two of everything. Would that mean first come, first served? Is there a lottery, or a drawing? Is Noah looking for the strongest? The most beautiful? The smartest, or the cleverest?"

"That's a lot of possibilities," Dustie said.

"You're right," the first porcupine said. "But he's only taking animals that don't get seasick. He checks them by spinning them around. If they don't look queasy, their eyes don't roll back, or they don't look pale, they get his OK."

Dustie and Woody both grinned.

"Aren't we lucky that termites don't get seasick?" Dustie said as they high-fived each other.

When their turn came, they both did well. Noah gave them the OK. They felt relieved and proud to represent their species.

Dustie and Woody started up the plank. Way up on top, Noah's son, Ham, was checking in each species as the animals came on board.

The termites heard loud clattering behind them.

"Watch out! Don't get stepped on!" shouted an ostrich from the deck of the ark. Woody jumped out of the way, pulling Dustie with him as two zebras thundered up the ramp.

"That was close," Dustie said.

They stayed on the outside edge of the ramp the rest of the way up. When they got to the top, Ham checked them in.

"Welcome! You two will live on the lower, lower, lower level. Take that ramp over there," he said.

"Thank you," Dustie said.

"See you later, Ham," Woody said.

||||||||||||||||||||||||||||||||||||||||||||||||||||||||||||||||||||||||||||||||||||||

"I'm hungry after that long walk," Woody said once they got all the way down to the level where they would be living.

"Me, too," said Dustie. As they looked around, a big smile spread across both faces.

"Oh, my golly," Woody said as he hugged Dustie. "We're surrounded by our favorite food. This whole boat is made of wood."

||||||||||||||||||||||||||||||||||||||||||||||||||||||||||||||||||||||||||||||||||||||

"I wonder who's in charge down here," Dustie said. She looked around to see if there was anyone she could ask. A moose looked her way.

"The humans are in charge," the moose said. "Noah, his wife, their three sons, and their wives will all live in quarters on the top deck. Each son is in charge of one of the three levels."

"That's a lot of work for each of them," Woody said.

"Who lives down here with us?" Dustie asked.

"Japheth is in charge down here. We have the biggest animals for ballast. Their weight will balance the ark when it starts to float. We also get any animal not assigned to the other levels," the moose said.

"I can imagine how stuffy and stinky it will be after a couple of months," Woody said. "Noah said we would be on board a long time."

"Air does flow down from the upper levels," the moose reassured him. "It flows down the ramps, and flows up and down openings Noah made inside the corners at both ends of the ark."

"One of those spots sounds like a great place to begin exploring," Dustie said. "We could move from level to level through those openings."

||||||||||||||||||||||||||||||||||||||||||||||||||||||||||||||||||||||||||||||||

While the rest of the animals came on board, Woody and Dustie checked out the lower, lower, lower level. They found where the food and fresh water were stored. There was enough for each animal for more than a year.

Finally, all the animals were aboard. Noah's sons pulled up the long ramp and fastened it to the deck. Loud sounds followed. Then everyone knew that the large door of the ark was shut tight.

The rain began to fall. It kept on falling. Dustie, Woody, and everyone else, waited for the water to rise and wondered about the future.

"I hope the size, the height, and the water displacement are big enough to float the ark," said Woody. "Do you think the calculations are right?"

Dustie took a deep breath before she responded. "I heard that the size of every creature was factored in, even small animals like us. Big animals, like the elephants, bisons, or water buffalo, got counted, too. We can only wait, hope, and see."

The termites set to work on finding the best place to settle down on the lower, lower, lower level. They stopped in front of the small cypress log that Noah had left for them to eat.

"I think Noah used cypress and oak to build the ark. Oak tastes better to me than cypress," Woody said.

"I like that better, too. Let's find a good oak board to eat," Dustie said. They moved to a spot on the outer wall of the ark.

"How about this spot?" Dustie asked. "It's about five feet up and toward the back. I like the privacy that it gives us."

"I like that spot, too," Woody said. "The wood still holds moisture. We won't have to look for water, or drink any of the precious water Noah has stored away."

"Let's get started," Dustie said. "Free room and board, yippee!"

Whenever they stopped eating and left their special board, Woody and Dustie wandered up and down the levels. During their first weeks on the ark, they discovered where all the animals were housed, and where each animal's food was stored. The termites were curious, not hungry. They already had more wood than they could eat.

Over time, they made friends with all kinds of creatures.

"Let's go all the way to the front of the ark today," Dustie said one morning.

Soon she and Woody were on their way. As they passed the aardvarks and leopards, Woody heard a sound.

"I think I hear someone crying," he said.

"It's the grizzly bears," Dustie said. "One looks really sad."

"What's wrong?" Woody asked. "What's happening?"

The bear turned to them, and wiped her nose with her paw.

"I'm homesick. I miss my family, and all my friends. I miss the smell of the forest, and the taste of blueberries."

"That must be hard," said Woody.

"Homesickness is a big problem on the ark. We don't have blueberries, but maybe the taste of honey will help," Dustie said. She pointed to the storeroom.

"We'll be right back," Woody said to the bear. Dustie led Woody to the spot in the storeroom that held the honey. They found a bay leaf, put some honey on it, and dragged it back to the bear.

"Here you go," Dustie said as they placed the leaf in front of her. First the bear sniffed it, then she flicked out her tongue, took a little of the honey into her mouth, and savored it.

Tears formed in the corners of the bear's eyes.

"My tears are of happiness, and remembering," she said.

"It's hard leaving your family, friends, and the security of home," said Dustie.

Woody nodded.

"It wasn't easy saying goodbye when we left our colony," he said. "I couldn't stand to think about not seeing our family and friends again. I still hold on to my hope that they might survive the flood after all."

That's what Dustie loved about Woody. He could feel his sadness and joy, and find words to express his feelings.

He gave the bear words of encouragement, and Dustie did too. The bear perked up.

"Thanks for the honey," she said. "And special thanks for stopping by."

"I'm glad we did that," Woody said, when they settled back down at their special board. "I feel really good when I can make a difference."

"I feel good, too," Dustie said. "And I'm also happy it's time for lunch."

"Aren't you glad termites don't sleep?" Woody asked.

"Yes, it means we can gnaw all day and night, if we want to," Dustie said.

They couldn't have been happier munching away on the delicious wood, slowly making a hole into the board. They did take breaks, to stretch their legs, to explore, to create stories to tell each other, and to have conversations with other animals.

||||||||||||||||||||||||||||||||||||||||||||||||||||||||||||||||||||||||||||||||||||

The next day Woody noticed that Dustie seemed especially quiet.

"Are you okay?" he asked.

"Woody, I've been thinking," Dustie said. "The creatures on the ark, the animals and the people, come in so many sizes and colors and make so many different sounds. But we're all in this together."

"That's right," Woody said. "And I've started to appreciate that underneath these differences, we're all the same on the inside. We're all connected somehow. No creature is better than the next."

A few days later, Dustie said, "There's something else I want to tell you, Woody. Even though we're all in this together, I'm still scared of the anteaters. With one flick of their long tongues, we could just disappear."

"I don't trust the predators, either," Woody said. "Moles, bats, and spiders eat us, too. We could be toast."

The two porcupines approached.

"We overheard your conversation," the one closest to Dustie said. "Maybe it would help to remember what Noah told us right after we came on board. He said there are three covenants on the ark that cannot be broken.

Woody closed his eyes and remembered:

> *Respect one another.*
>
> *Do not harm one another.*
>
> *Do not eat one another.*

"We can disagree as long as we respectfully listen to each other," the other porcupine chimed in. "We can't just throw someone overboard for disagreeing, or eat them because they're delicious."

Woody and Dustie started to feel better. The porcupines were right. The animals all understood that they needed to work together to survive. The termites relaxed a little, knowing that they were off limits, and not on someone's menu.

Most of the time while they were on the ark, the animals rested, slept, or had conversations with each other. Sometimes they allowed themselves to think about what it would be like to leave the ark, to venture out to parts of this unexplored new world, and to start a family.

|||||||||||||||||||||||||||||||||||||||||||||||||||||||||||||||||||||||||||||||||||||||||

All the humans on board shared the work of caring for the animals. Noah's sons, Shem, Ham, and Japheth, did the heavy lifting. Each brought food and water to his area every day, and removed any soiled hay. If one brother finished his work early, he would ask if the others needed his help.

After a few weeks, Japheth noticed sawdust on the floor of the lower, lower, lower level, near the back of the ark. He stopped and stared.

"I wonder why I didn't notice this before," he said to himself. He swept it away and decided to check again the next day. If there were still signs of something eating away at the wood, he would investigate further.

A few hours later, Dustie looked out of the hole where they were eating.

"Hey, Woody, there's no sawdust below our hole," she said.

"How could that be? There's always sawdust wherever we eat," Woody said. "Could Japheth have cleaned it up?"

They looked at each other in horror. They had neglected the most important rule in the termite world: *When you eat in a structure built by humans, do not leave any evidence.* What could they do?

"I have an idea," Dustie said. "Every morning before Japheth is awake, we'll remove the sawdust from the night before."

"We'll take it to a distant area and spread it around," Woody said. They both smiled in relief. After a few days, it was just part of their routine.

"Let's explore two levels up again," Dustie said one morning. Woody smiled.

"I liked it up there, too," he said.

They chatted with the monkeys and the field mice. As they left their new friends, another sound caught Woody's attention.

"Did you hear that?" he asked.

"It sounds like someone moaning," Dustie said. They turned a corner and saw a seagull holding his stomach. He looked ill. Even his beak was pale.

"That bird looks seasick! How can that be?" Dustie exclaimed. "Noah checked everyone on board for that possibility. How did this get by him?"

"I'm curious, and sometimes nosy," Woody said. "Let's go find out." They moved closer.

"Are you really seasick?" Dustie asked the seagull.

The bird nodded sadly and huddled closer to the other seagull.

"I wanted to make sure that the two of us got on board together," he said. "I practiced and practiced spinning around and holding my breath at the same time. I did it for days before getting in line with my mate. It worked. It helped me from feeling seasick during the test. But I can't spend all day and night holding my breath on the ark. The nausea just keeps getting worse."

"That sounds terrible," Dustie said. Then Woody had an idea.

"Ginger root!" Woody said to Dustie. "Remember when we were young termites? They told us that eating some ginger would help calm our stomachs."

"Maybe it will work for seagulls, too," Dustie said.

Dustie and Woody went to where the herbs and spices were stored. They found some ginger root, and rolled a piece back to the seagull.

"We'll check back with you in a few days," Woody said.

When they returned, the seagull looked much better.

"Thank you," he said. "As long as I nibble a little ginger each day, I feel fine."

For 40 days and 40 nights, the animals heard the rain pounding against the ark. They felt the constant rocking, and heard the rain hitting the roof and sides of the ark. It was an ordinary part of the new life they were all living.

"Something is strange," Woody said when he woke up on the 41st morning. "Something is missing."

"Oh, it's not raining!" Dustie exclaimed. Woody began to jump for joy. They heard the humans cheering on the upper deck. All the other animals joined in. Then, over the stamping of hooves and the flapping of wings, Dustie and Woody heard Noah shouting.

"Start bringing the animals up to the top level to get some fresh air! It will help them to move their legs, and rebuild their strength."

"They'll be able to look around, too," his wife said.

‖‖

At first, all anyone could see was water, sky, and sunshine, but this was more than okay with both the animals and the people. Being out of their confined spaces and seeing the sunlight lifted everyone's mood.

"Look at the smiles on those faces," Dustie said as Japheth brought the meerkats and a few other animals back down to the lower, lower, lower level.

Woody and Dustie didn't feel that they had to go out onto the deck, though. Surrounded by wood, they were already in their element. They just stayed positive, and kept gnawing.

Noah and his sons tried to bring as many animals as they could up from the levels each day. Sometimes a sore hoof, or a bad tooth, meant a few animals needed special care. Every day many animals needed to be brushed, groomed, hugged, patted, or scratched behind the ears.

The people bonded with the animals as they worked. The animals liked seeing them and always enjoyed their company. No one knew how long they would still be living on the ark, since the waters had to recede and the earth needed to dry out. Being seen and acknowledged went a long way toward helping everyone feel at ease.

|||||||||||||||||||||||||||||||||||||||||||||||||||||||||||||||||||||||||||||||||||||||||||

As time went on, whenever the animals were on deck, they scanned the flood waters for evidence that others had survived. One morning, when Woody and Dustie were cleaning up the sawdust in front of their hole, they felt the sadness around them. They looked up and saw the moose. She looked very unhappy.

"What happened?" Dustie said.

"Nobody else made it," the moose said. "They're all gone."

"What do you mean, all gone?" Woody said.

"There's got to be somebody left," Dustie said.

"There's only water out there. Everyone else is really gone," the moose said gently. She heaved a great sigh.

Woody and Dustie were silent. Without another word, they slowly went back to their hole.

"You mean we're really the only termites left?" Woody asked.

"It's what we hoped wouldn't be true, even though that's why we're here," Dustie said with tears running down her face. "I want to remember our friends and family. I want to remember the world we knew. I miss them so."

She and Woody talked, and cried, and held each other. They were too sad to eat that day.

||||||||||||||||||||||||||||||||||||||||||||||||||||||||||||||||||||||||||||||||

After another month or so, as Dustie and Woody walked on the lower, lower, lower level, they noticed a lion pacing about, and pulling on his mane. He looked very frightened. His pupils were large, and he was breathing fast.

"I can't stand this any longer," the lion said. "I've got to get out of here. I feel so closed in."

Dustie and Woody could sense the lion's panic. They went to Japheth, and told him what they had seen.

"Maybe you could move the lion and his mate up to the upper level to live. They'll have more room to move around," Woody said.

"They'll be happier, too," Dustie said.

The very next day, they saw Japheth and the lions pass by on their way to the ramp leading to the higher levels.

"Japheth did it!" the termites hollered to each other. "He took our advice!"

||||||||||||||||||||||||||||||||||||||||||||||||||||||||||||||||||||||||||||||||||||||||||||||||||

A few days later, Noah's wife grabbed her husband's arm while they were walking on the upper deck.

"Look! Over there!" She pointed off to the right. "Is that…"

"The very first land," Noah said. They held each other and stared out across the water for a silent moment. Then Noah called to their sons and their wives.

"Hurry, come up here! We see land!"

"They see land!" the lions said to each other. They started to roar with glee.

The other animals heard the lions roar and the humans' footsteps running up the ramps.

"What's that all about?" one of the bison asked from the lower, lower, lower level.

"Noah says he sees land," one of the porcupines said. "And the lions believe him."

Excitement rippled through all the animals on the ark.

Slowly, slowly, the water level went further down. Mountain tops appeared, and the ark settled on Mount Ararat. There was nothing left for anyone to do but wait for the earth to dry out.

They waited a long, long time.

One day, Noah's wife heard their sons talking to their father.

"I wonder how much longer it will be before we can leave," Japheth said. "I want to feel the earth under my feet again."

"I agree with you. I'm really ready to get off, too," Shem said. "How will we know when there's enough dry land?"

"Maybe the animals will know before we do," Noah said. "The birds seem more restless than before."

"Maybe so, but how will they tell us?" Ham asked.

"I have an idea," their mother said. "What about sending out a pair of birds? If there are no living trees for them to nest in, they'll come back to the ark."

The rest of the family thought that was a good idea.

"I'll send out the pair of doves," Noah said.

"But why send both of them?" Ham asked.

"So that they can stay together and support each other," Noah responded.

||||||||||||||||||||||||||||||||||||||||||||||||||||||||||||||||||||||||||||||||||||

At first the birds returned every night. Once, they were gone for a few days. When they returned, one carried a leaf from an olive branch in her beak. Everybody felt hopeful. When the birds flew off again and didn't return, everyone missed them, but felt even more hopeful. It was easier to wait now.

||||||||||||||||||||||||||||||||||||||||||||||||||||||||||||||||||||||||||||||||||||

One night Noah woke so suddenly that he remembered only a part of the dream he was having. Something about it was gnawing away at him. In the dream, he saw himself spinning two termites, then watching them walk up the long ramp into the ark.

He had never thought about them again. Where were they? Why hadn't he seen them about? He had heard some very good things about two small creatures. They had helped a bear, a seagull, and a lion. Could those helpers be the termites? Noah got up from his straw mat and headed for the lower, lower, lower level.

As he descended the last ramp and moved toward the back of the ark, Noah raised his oil lamp high so he could see better. He looked around but didn't see anything unusual. What were those termites' names? Woody and ……. Dustie! That was it!

"Woody! Dustie!" Noah called out several times. Out of the corner of his eye, he saw some movement. He stepped closer and saw the termites emerge from a small hole in the side of the ark. A thin ray of light was coming in. Noah also felt air moving on the side of his face. His oil lamp flickered a little.

Sure enough, the termites had successfully gnawed their way through the side of the ark. Noah breathed a sigh of relief. There was no danger of taking on water. Taking on air and light was a different story. Why hadn't he thought of cutting holes to let light and air in down here? And on the other levels, too, for that matter. Noah sat down next to the hole, and spoke quietly to Woody and Dustie.

"You've been gnawing away for months and no one knew what you were doing all that time. I'm just glad that you didn't gnaw through that board during the heavy rains. And I'm grateful you reached out to those in distress during those tough times." Before Noah could get the next words out, Dustie took a step forward.

"We were just doing what we do best," she said. Noah and Woody both smiled.

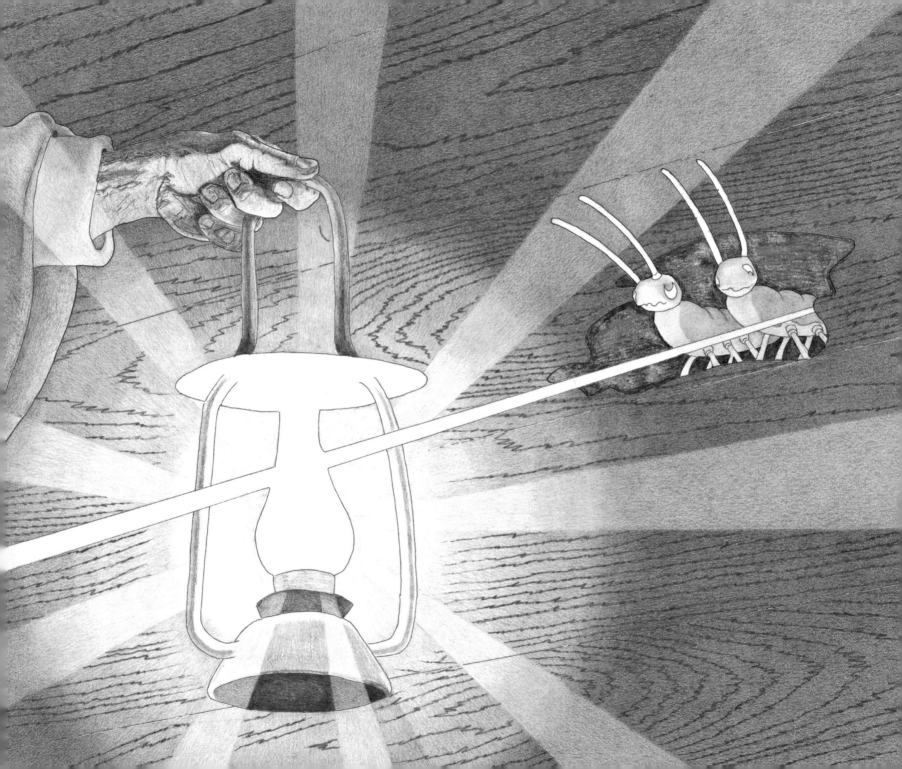

"You two have accomplished something that no one else on board had thought of, or could have done. You created a window to the outside. Do you mind if my sons enlarge this opening? Then everyone can see out, and feel the air on their faces."

Woody and Dustie looked at each other, and grinned even wider.

"Go for it," they said in unison.

"And I know just the spot for us to start eating again," Dustie said.

"Enjoy your meal," Noah said. He got up and headed for the ramp. As he passed the porcupines, he reached down and patted them both on the head.

"Come see us again," Woody called.

"Don't be a stranger," Dustie said.

They went to the other side of the lower, lower, lower level, and started gnawing away.

"We won't ever have to remove the sawdust in front of our hole again," Woody said.

||||||||||||||||||||||||||||||||||||||||||||||||||||||||||||||||||||||||||||||||||||||||||

The porcupines got word out to all the animals about what Woody and Dustie had done, and what Noah had decided. That way none of the animals were surprised by the noise that Japheth made as he enlarged the first hole. All of them were delighted when Ham and Shem began work on other windows on the other side of the ark.

Later that day, one of the anteaters moved closer to where Dustie and Woody were eating. They tensed a little as the anteater approached.

"I really look up to you," the anteater said. "That's not easy to do, since I have to physically look down to see you. Thanks for all you've done. All of the animals have talked about your kindness. We appreciate you."

"Wow! Thanks for telling us," Dustie said.

The months came and went. Noah's sons made more openings on all three levels. The darkness that had been so thick faded as the light came in. The animals loved looking out, hearing the wind, and seeing clouds move by.

‖‖‖

One evening, while out on a stroll with Dustie, Woody heard someone sneezing.

"That doesn't sound good," he said. "Let's check it out."

It was the porcupine who had helped them when they had first gotten in line outside the ark.

"What's making you sneeze so much?" asked Dustie.

"I'm not sure," said the porcupine. She sneezed again, three times. Quills shot out with each sneeze. Woody and Dustie both ducked.

"It could be something around us, like the dust, or the dander built up on that bison over there," said the second porcupine.

Woody looked around and saw the bison standing nearby. He started to say something, and then sneezed, too. After wiping his nose, he said, "Maybe you just need to move a little further away from them."

"Good idea," said Dustie, as the two porcupines moved a few stalls closer to a window.

||||||||||||||||||||||||||||||||||||||||||||||||||||||||||||||||||||||||||||||||||||||||||

Soon the animals could see the earth had dried. Plants were growing again. Everyone could feel the excitement build as they anticipated leaving. They could already imagine moving out into this new world.

That day finally came.

"Let's plan to be the last ones off," Woody said as they climbed to the upper deck.

"That way we won't be stepped on," Dustie said. They stood side by side at the top of the ramp. As the anteaters walked by, they nodded their heads to Woody and Dustie in respect.

Woody and Dustie felt sad as they waved goodbye to the last of the friends they had made on the ark. All the other animals were gone. The ark was empty.

"It's time to go," Dustie said. The termites hesitated as they looked out onto the mountain range. In the distance, an arc of colors glowed in the sky.

"Look at all those colors!" Woody said.

"I like the orange part best," Dustie said.

"I like the whole thing," Woody said.

"Beautiful," Dustie whispered. They stared up toward the sky.

"Wait a minute," Woody said after awhile. "Why should we go? Why leave this wonderful food supply that was our home for the past year?"

"You're right!" Dustie said. "We're already home. Let's stay right here."

A wave of happiness washed over both of them. Woody reached out and took her hand. Together, they turned and went back inside.

Woody and Dustie's offspring, their offspring, and generation after generation of termites, continued to eat away at the ark. Today, after thousands of years, little of it remains. That's why explorers seeking the ark have had trouble finding it. There just isn't very much left to find.

THE END